GOD'S WORLD MAKES ME FEEL

GOD'S WORLD
MAKES ME
FEEL SO

LITTLE

Written and illustrated by
HELEN CASWELL

Abingdon Press
Nashville

GOD'S WORLD MAKES ME FEEL SO LITTLE

Library of Congress Cataloging in Publication Data

Caswell, Helen Rayburn.
  God's World makes me feel so little.
  1. Children—Religious life—Juvenile literature.
  I. Title.
  BV4571.2.C38   1985   242'.62   84-14545
              ISBN 0-687-15510-X

PRINTED IN HONG KONG

For Elizabeth, Teresa, and Devin
and for all the little people
who may sometimes wonder if
God cares about them. Perhaps these
words and pictures will
help them to see that God knows
all about them, and loves them,
every one.

Sometimes I feel so little . . .

In the city you would hardly notice me at all.

Everyone, it seems, is very tall,
compared to me.

No matter where I go, it is the same.

The ocean, at the seashore,
is so big, I can't see where it ends.

And in the forest, the trees grow up so high that I can't see the tops.

The sky goes on forever, full of great
tremendous clouds, and a million
trillion stars, at least.

It makes me wonder—
does God know that I'm here?

Can he care anything about me, really,
when I'm so little?

But then I think of other little things.
My kitten's a lot smaller than me.

And then there are the mice,
and little birds,

and grasshoppers, and worms,

and tiny little flowers in the grass.

When I see how much care God took to make
a tiny butterfly, I know I'm not so little,
after all, as far as God's concerned.

He loves me just the way I am.